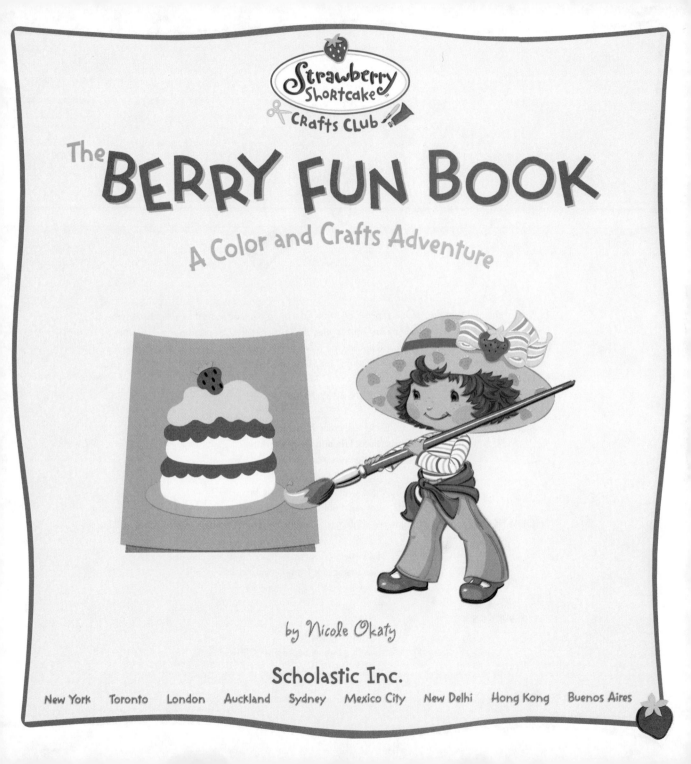

Strawberry Shortcake™
Crafts Club

The BERRY FUN BOOK

A Color and Crafts Adventure

by Nicole Okaty

Scholastic Inc.

New York   Toronto   London   Auckland   Sydney   Mexico City   New Delhi   Hong Kong   Buenos Aires

ISBN 0-439-70309-3

Designer: Emily Muschinske
Illustrations: Lisa and Terry Workman
Photographs: Nicole Okaty

12 11 10 9 8 7 6 5 4 3 2 1   4 5 6 7 8 9/0

Printed in the U.S.A.
First Scholastic printing, September 2004

TABLE of CONTENTS

Get Ready for a
Berry Sweet Strawberry Adventure!

Hi, I'm Strawberry Shortcake! I live in Strawberryland, where you can find sweet strawberries in all shapes and sizes. One of the largest berries in Strawberryland is my Berry Happy Home, where I live with my little sister, Apple Dumplin', and my sweet and cuddly pets, Pupcake and Custard. Welcome to my berry special world!

In this strawberry-filled book, you'll find some of my favorite strawberry projects and berrylicious recipes. In Strawberryland, it's fun to make crafts, share sweet treats, and play games together! I hope you'll be my new friend and join me on this berry fun color and crafts adventure!

Strawberry Shortcake's Tips for Getting Started

1. Set up your workspace and try to keep it berry neat!

2. Before you start each project, ask an adult to help you collect all the materials you'll need.

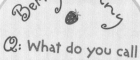

3. Whenever you see this picture throughout the book, it means that you can find what you need in your craft kit!

4. A lot of the materials that you'll need can be found around your house. You can get other supplies at a grocery or craft store.

5. You may need an adult's help with some activities in the book. Whenever you see this symbol, you'll know to ask for help.

Did you know that dreaming of strawberries is a sign of sweet things to come? There's a lot more **strawberry** fun coming up in the pages of this book!

Getting Ready to Paint

1. Put on an apron or smock to keep your clothes berry neat.

2. Spread newspaper on the workspace where you will paint.

3. Keep paper towels handy—for clean up or spills.

4. When finger painting, keep a small bowl of water nearby to dip your hands in, before using another color of paint. (If you prefer to paint with a paintbrush, then use the bowl of water for rinsing the brush.)

Mixing Colors

Did you know that when you mix two different colors of paint together, you can make a whole new color? If you mix red paint with white paint, you can make strawberry pink!

You'll get to make pink and other colors in the berry special projects in this book!

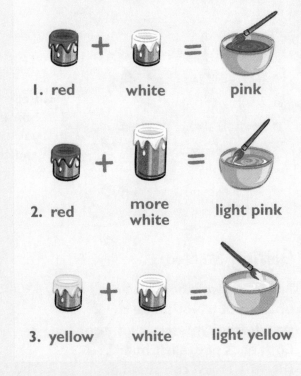

1. red   white   pink

2. red   more white   light pink

3. yellow   white   light yellow

Turn the page to see the wonderful colors in my world!

Fun with Felt

Strawberry Shortcake's Berry Happy Home (Outside)

Strawberryland comes to life when you create my berry happy home using stickers and felt!

What You Need

- Two-sided felt board
- 2 felt board stands
- Reusable sticker sheet
- 2 Strawberry Shortcake felt dolls
- Felt furniture: Armchair, table, and chair

Getting Started:

Hold the two-sided felt board up in front of you. Slide the 2 stands from your craft kit into both ends of the felt board, so that the board can stand on its own.

1. Let's start by decorating the outside of my home—the red side of the felt board. Can you use the stickers to add my front door and the two flower-box picture windows?

2. You can add my pineapple-shaped light next to the front door to greet guests at night!

5

3. What else can you add? How about putting some apples in the apple tree?

4. Can you add some flowers and strawberries around my front porch? They'll smell so berry sweet!

5. Will my lovable dog, Pupcake, get into trouble in the yard?

6. What else can you add outside my house? How about the watering can?

Can you spot me on the felt board?

Turn the page to decorate the inside of my house!

Strawberry Shortcake's Berry Happy Home (Inside)

*L*et's decorate the inside of my berry happy home—the pink side of your felt board!

1. Can you help me create a cozy room with my furniture from your craft kit?

3. Can you find my teapot? Place it on the stovetop.

2. Let's hang the curtains on the picture window.

4. Will my *purrfectly* sweet cat, Custard, nap by the stove?

5. Add a bowl of fresh-picked berries to the table and my favorite dessert, strawberry shortcake!

6. Help me place the reading lamp over my armchair.

7. Add my strawberry clock and bookshelf to the wall. Don't forget to put the books on the bookshelf!

Dressing Up:

You'll find two Strawberry Shortcake felt dolls (one that is sitting and one that is standing) in your craft kit.

It's so berry fun to get dressed up! On your sticker sheet, you'll find some of my favorite outfits.

Here's More: At night, I like to wear my pajamas, sit in my comfy chair, and read a berry good bedtime story.

What other scenes can you create?

Turn the page to make a project that you'll love to wear!

Strawberry Shortcake's Friendship Bracelet

Make and wear this bracelet as a gift from me to you!

What You Need

- Elastic cord
- Scissors
- Tape
- Strawberry-scented beads (red, fuchsia, and light pink)
- Small bowl

2. Tie a knot about ¹/₂-inch in on one end of the cord. Tape the knot onto your workspace to help hold it in place.

1. Take the elastic cord from your craft kit and wrap it around your wrist. With an adult's help, measure and cut the cord about 1-inch past where it meets your wrist.

3. Pour your red, fuchsia, and light pink strawberry-scented beads into a small bowl so that they won't roll away.

4. **What kind of pretty pattern will you make on your bracelet? String the beads onto the cord.**

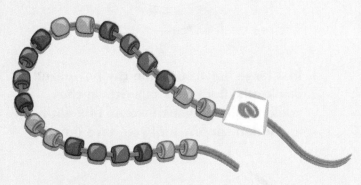

5. **Create a colorful pattern of your berry own! Continue adding beads until you've almost filled your bracelet.**

6. **Remove the tape from your workspace. Tie the two ends of your bracelet together by making a double knot.**

7. **Trim the ends of the cord with scissors and slip your strawberry bracelet onto your wrist!**

For more fruity fun, turn the page!

Scent-sational Strawberry Dough

This strawberry-scented dough is fun
to sculpt with and fun to smell!

What You Need

- 1 packet of unsweetened Kool-Aid® or other unsweetened strawberry-powdered drink mix (.13 ounces)
- 10 ounces flour
- 1/3 cup salt
- 1 tablespoon cooking oil
- 1/2 cup warm water from the tap
- Food coloring (in red and green)
- Pencil
- Utensils: Large bowl, wooden spoon, measuring cups and spoons

1. In a large bowl, combine the powdered drink mix, flour, and salt. Stir in the cooking oil and warm water. Mix with a wooden spoon, until you have dough.

2. Knead the dough with your hands on a lightly floured surface. The dough will become firm in about 3 minutes.

Separate the dough into two pieces, one large and one small. The large piece should be about the size of an apple, and the small piece about the size of a plum.

. To make strawberries, add 7 to 8 drops of red food coloring to the large dough. Mold with your hands, until the color is blended in (about 5 minutes).

. To make leaves and stems, add 3 to 4 drops of green food coloring to the small dough. Mold with your hands, until the color is blended in (about 3 minutes).

6. Now it's time to make your own berries! Roll the red dough into different-sized balls. Use a pencil to make seed-like impressions in the dough, and add green leaves and curly stems to the tops.

To make the colors of your **red berries** and **green leaves** deeper, add more drops of food coloring. You can also use sweetened strawberry-powdered drink mix, but it will make your dough a little sticky!

Turn the page for some strawberry fun and games!

Strawberryland Near and Far

Take a close look at these pictures from my photo album.

My little sister, Apple Dumplin', took these pictures. She got too close, so you can't always tell what you are looking at! The six pictures on this page show close-up views. The six pictures on the next page are shown just right. Can you match the near and far pictures of the same scene?

1.

2.

3.

4.

5.

6.

A.

B.

C.

D.

E.

F.

See page 38 for the answers.)

Turn the page to find
a strawberry patch
in full bloom!

Strawberry Patch Hunt

Can you help me find the five unusual berries hidden in my strawberry patch?

Here is a strawberry riddle. Can you find everything mentioned in the picture?

I spy two strawberries that are bigger than the rest and a very tiny strawberry.

I spy a strawberry with extra-big leaves and a berry that isn't a strawberry.

What else do you see?

Can you find a ladybug, a butterfly, and a bumblebee?

(Turn to page 38 for the answers.)

Now, turn the page for some finger-printing fun!

17

Mix It Up: Fun with Paint

Strawberry Shortcake's Blooming Berry Patch

You can make your own berry patch with rows of sweet strawberries!

What You Need

- Washable paint (in red and white)
- 8-½ x 11-inch sheet of light green paper
- Black fine-point marker
- Green fine-point marker
- Optional: Yellow paint

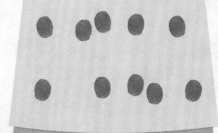

2. Now, make another row of red prints across the bottom of your paper. Let the prints dry completely.

1. To paint a row of strawberries, dip your pointer finger into the red paint and make a row of fingerprints across the top of your paper.

3. To paint flowers, dip your pinkie finger into the white paint and make a print next to a strawberry. Add more white prints (flowers) around your rows of strawberries. Let dry.

4. If you have yellow paint, make small prints in the center of the white ones to add color to your flowers. Let dry.

5. Using the black marker, draw dots (for seeds) on your strawberries.

6. Using the green marker, draw leaves on top of your strawberries and around your flowers.

7. Add curly stems and vines connecting your berries, if you like.

Did you know that Arizona, Arkansas, and California all have towns named Strawberry? Also, there's a town named Strawberry Point in Iowa, which is the home of the world's largest strawberry sculpture!

Turn the page to make a postcard that you can send (or give) to your berry best friend!

Strawberry Shortcake's Fingerprint Postcards

These strawberries will give your cards a berry special touch!

What You Need

- Red washable paint
- 5 x 4-inch white card stock or plain postcards
- Black fine-point marker
- Green fine-point marker

2. Using the black marker, draw dots (seeds) on your strawberries.

1. To paint strawberries, dip your pointer finger into the red paint and make a fingerprint on the bottom of the message side of your postcard. Add a few more prints. Then, let the prints dry completely.

3. Using the green marker, add the leaves and stems.

4. Draw an "s"-shaped line down the center of your postcard (the "s" is for strawberries). Later, you can write your message on the left side of the postcard and your friend's address on the right.

5. Now, flip your postcard over to the front side to decorate it with fingerprint strawberries. Will you paint one strawberry or a whole patch? Will you add flowers and vines?

Here's More: Write a note to your berry best friend, add a postage stamp, and send the postcard in the mail. Or, make your own postage stamp and deliver the postcard to your friend yourself. You'll both be berry glad you did!

Dear Angel Cake,

I will come to visit you in your cake shop soon! Have a berry nice day!

Your berry best friend, Strawberry Shortcake

Strawberry Shortcake
Strawberryland

Angel Cake
Cakewalk

Turn the page for a tasty treat that looks yummy enough to eat!

Strawberry Shortcake's Berry Best Cake

*C*an you paint a picture of my berry favorite dessert?
How many layers will your strawberry shortcake be?

What You Need

- Washable paints
  (in red and white)
- Yellow paint
- Paper plate
- Paintbrush
- Pink construction paper
- Green fine-point marker
- Black fine-point marker

2. **Now let's start from the top!
   Lay your pink construction paper
   down the tall way. With your
   paintbrush, paint a red strawberry
   shape at the top of the paper.**

1. **Arrange the paint on a paper plate using
   your paintbrush: Red for the berries, light
   pink for the whipped cream, and light
   yellow for the shortcake. (See page 5
   for help mixing your colors!)**

3. **Paint a big blob of light pink
   whipped cream right under
   the berry.**

4. Add a layer of red strawberries under the whipped cream.

5. With the light yellow paint, add a shortcake layer.

6. Add more red berries under the shortcake. Then, paint the bottom layer of the cake yellow! Let dry.

7. Draw a plate. Add leaves and a stem to your strawberry topper. Use the black marker to draw some dots (seeds) on your berries.

You can also paint this picture from the bottom to the top! Or use your finger instead of a brush to paint the shortcake layers!

Hold on to your hat! Turn the page for another berry fun craft.

Strawberry Shortcake's Happy Hat

I never go anywhere without my berry special hat.
Now, you can make and wear a hat just like mine!

What You Need

- 2 white paper bowls
- 1 large white paper plate
- Pencil with an eraser
- Scissors
- Washable paint (red and white)
- Paintbrush
- Stapler or tape
- 1 yard of red ribbon or crepe paper streamers, cut in half
- White craft glue or school glue
- Optional: Striped bow or paper bow, pom-poms, paper streamers, stickers

1. Center one paper bowl upside down on top of an upside down paper plate. Use your pencil to trace around the bowl.

2. By following your tracing, cut the circle out from the middle of the plate, staying $1/2$-inch in from the line.

3. Mix some red and white paint together in the other paper bowl, to make a bright shade of pink.

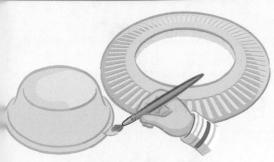

Paint the paper plate ring (the brim of the hat) and the bowl pink, as shown.

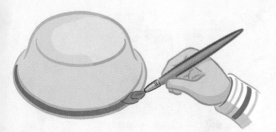

Paint the outer rim of the bowl red. Let dry.

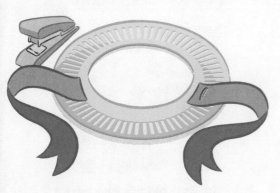

5. To create hat ties, staple or tape an 18-inch piece of ribbon to each side of your hat's brim.

7. Put glue on the inner rim of the bowl and attach it to your hat's brim. Let dry.

Here's More: You can decorate your hat with bows, pom-poms, paper streamers, or stickers.

How many seeds do you think a strawberry has? Turn the page to find out.

Strawberry Shortcake's Berrylicious-Looking Strawberry

Have you ever picked your own strawberries from a patch? This berry looks really ripe!

What You Need

- Construction paper (2 sheets of pink, 1 red, and 1 green)
- Pencil with an eraser
- Craft glue or glue stick

2. Tear half of the red construction paper into 1/2-inch or smaller pieces.

1. What shape will your strawberry be? Take a pink sheet of construction paper and turn it sideways. Use your pencil to draw a large strawberry shape with leaves in the center.

3. Glue the red pieces inside the strawberry, one at a time, until the entire berry is covered.

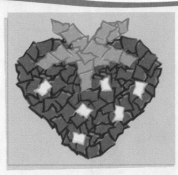

Now it's time for the leaves! Tear a small amount of the green construction paper into ¹/₂-inch or smaller pieces.

6. Tear 7 to 10 tiny pieces of pink construction paper and glue them on top of your strawberry to make the seeds.

Glue the green pieces inside the leaves.

Did you know that the average strawberry has 200 seeds? You would have to tear a lot of paper to make that many seeds for your berrylicious berry!

Here's More: You can make a pink strawberry with red seeds, too! Or, make a strawberry using any colors you choose.

There is such a nice breeze in Strawberryland today. Turn the page for a high-flying adventure!

Strawberry Shortcake's Sweet Flying Kite

You can make this berry sweet kite take flight! Up, up, and away!

What You Need

- 1 sheet of light-blue construction paper
- Pencil with an eraser
- Markers or crayons (red, green, black)
- 7-inch yarn or string
- White craft glue or school glue
- Ribbon or paper bows

2. Color in the strawberry, with the red marker or crayon.

1. Draw a strawberry with leaves near the top of your sky-blue construction paper.

3. Color in the strawberry's leaves, with the green marker or crayon.

4. Draw black dots (seeds) on your strawberry kite.

5. To make the tail of your kite, lay out your 7-inch yarn or string, from the bottom of your kite to the end of the paper. Glue it in place.

6. Decorate your kite with ribbons or paper bows, if you like.

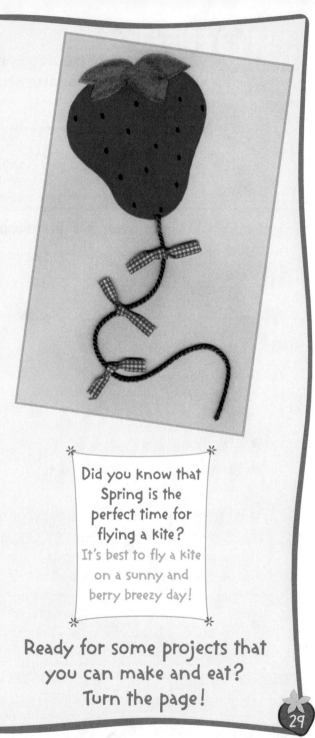

Did you know that
Spring is the
perfect time for
flying a kite?
It's best to fly a kite
on a sunny and
berry breezy day!

Ready for some projects that
you can make and eat?
Turn the page!

Here are some yummy recipes that you can make and share with your berry best friends!

Cool n' Sweet Strawberry Shortcakes

These no-bake mini shortcakes are berry fun to make. Enjoy them with your berry best friends!

What You Need

- 1 pint fresh strawberries or 15-20 frozen strawberries, thawed
- 2 teaspoons sugar
- 6 vanilla cupcakes without frosting (and without liners)
- Whipped cream (canned or make your own, on page 32)
- Utensils: Paper towel, cutting knife, small bowl, spoon, bread knife, serving dish
- Serves: 6 berry sweet friends

1. Put aside 6 berrylicious strawberries to decorate the top of your mini cakes. Wash them and pat them dry with a paper towel.

Did you know it's best to wash fresh strawberries just before you use them? It's also best to remove the stems after you've washed them, so that the berries don't lose their sweet flavor before you eat them.

2. Wash the rest of your berries. (You should have about 9 to 14 berries.) Then remove the stems and slice the fruit.

3. In the small bowl, sprinkle 2 teaspoons of sugar on the berries, and stir. Let the mixture sit at least 5 minutes to bring out the berries' juices.

4. Slice the cupcakes in half.

5. Place the bottom slices of the cupcakes on a serving dish. Add a spoonful of berries to each cupcake. Top with a layer of whipped cream.

6. Cover each cupcake with the top cupcake slice. Add more berries and whipped cream.

(continues)

7. Decorate each mini cake with one more berrylicious strawberry!

Here's More: You can use biscuits or shortcake dessert shells instead of vanilla cupcakes! Or, you can slice a pound cake and use cookie cutters to make the shortcake's shape. Once you have your cake, just decorate with strawberries and whipped cream.

Cool n' Sweet Homemade Whipped Cream

What You Need

- 1 cup heavy whipping cream, chilled
- 1 ½ tablespoons confectioner's sugar
- ½ teaspoons pure vanilla extract
- Utensils: Measuring spoons and cups, large plastic jar with lid, spoon

1. Pour the heavy whipping cream, sugar, and vanilla extract into a plastic jar.

2. Twist the lid on the jar as tightly as you can, and then shake, shake, shake, until the filling becomes soft, white, and fluffy—like a cloud! (Shake for about 5 to 10 minutes.)

3. Now you can spoon some of your whipped cream onto your berrylicious cakes!

Very Berry Strawberry Lemonade

This sweet and slushy lemonade is perfect to share on a sunny day!

What You Need

- 12-ounce can of frozen lemonade concentrate, partially thawed
- 4 to 5 cans of water (measured in your lemonade can)
- 10 frozen strawberries, partially thawed
- Utensils: Large spoon, pitcher or punch bowl
- Serves: 10 berry cool friends

1. Using the large spoon, mix together the lemonade concentrate and the cans of water in a pitcher or punch bowl.

2. Stir in the 10 partially thawed strawberries.

3. Serve this "party punch in a pretty pitcher or punch bowl!" See if you can say that—5 times berry fast!

What else can you make to eat that's perfectly pink? Turn the page to see!

33

Strawberry Shortcake's Perfectly Pink Cream Cheese

This strawberry spread tastes yummylicious on mini bagels, toast, or rice cakes!

What You Need

- 10 fresh strawberries or frozen berries, thawed
- 3 teaspoons sugar
- 8 ounces cream cheese, softened
- Mini bagels, toast, or rice cakes
- Utensils: Butter knife, small bowl, spoon, medium-sized bowl, potato masher or wooden spoon
- Serves: 10 to 12 berry nice friends

1. **Wash 10 strawberries, remove the stems, and slice.**

2. **In a small bowl, sprinkle 3 teaspoons of sugar on the berries, and stir. Let the mixture sit at least 5 minutes to bring out the berries' juices.**

5. Spread your pink cream cheese onto mini bagels, toast, or rice cakes. Yummy!

3. In a medium-sized bowl, soften the cream cheese with a potato masher or wooden spoon.

4. Add the berries to the cream cheese and mix until smooth.

Here's More: You can dip fresh strawberries into your strawberry cream cheese. Yummylicious!

Turn the page to make another berrylicious snack.
This one you can wear as a necklace!

Strawberry Shortcake's Twist Necklace

This candy necklace is as much fun to make as it is to eat!

What You Need

- Scissors
- 4 to 5 strawberry-flavored licorice twists
- 30-inches clear craft lace or dental floss

1. Cut the ends off the strawberry-flavored licorice twists.

2. Snip the strawberry twists into 1-inch pieces or tubes.

3. String the tubes of strawberry twists onto your craft lace or dental floss.

4. Tie your edible necklace into a knot and wear it! How long do you think it will take you to eat off all the candy?

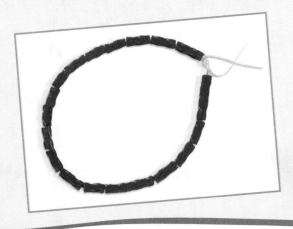

Strawberry Shortcake's Ice Pops

These frozen treats are simply scrumptious and berry sweet to eat!

What You Need

- 1 pint fresh strawberries
- Popsicle sticks
- 1 large sealable bag
- Utensils: Strainer, paper towels

3. Place the strawberry pops into a sealable bag.

1. Wash the strawberries and place them into a strainer lined with paper towels. Remove each strawberry's stem.

2. Slide a popsicle stick into the top of each strawberry (the place that you just removed the stems from).

4. Freeze until solid, for about 3 hours.

Strawberry Shortcake's Answer Page

Strawberryland Near and Far (pages 14 and 15)

1. C.
2. A.
3. E.
4. B.
5. D.
6. F.

Strawberry Patch Hunt (pages 16 and 17)

tiny berry

ladybug

butterfly

raspberry
(berry that isn't
a strawberry)

bumblebee

berry with
extra-big
leaves

2 big berries

38

More
Strawberryland Adventures Coming Soon!

To My Berry Sweet New Friend,

Thank you for coming with me on this color and crafts adventure! I hope you had a berry fun time in Strawberryland. I am really happy to have a new friend as sweet as you. Come back for more berry fun adventures soon!

Your berry best new friend,

Strawberry Shortcake